ORTHODOX ICON COLORING BOOK

SIMON OSKOLNIY

Pubished by Trinity Press

Printed in the United States of America
ISBN: 978-1619494831

CONTENTS

Plate 1. Andrei Rublev, "Trinity" (end of the 14th — beginning of the 15th century) /Андрей Рублёв, «Троица»/

Andrei Rublev was a medieval Russian painter of Orthodox icons and frescos. One of the masterpieces he created was "Trinity," an icon based on a story from the Book of Genesis called "The Hospitality of Abraham." It depicts three angels visiting Abraham at the Oak of Mamre to tell him that Sarah would soon give birth to a son. Abraham and Sarah are not featured in Rublev's icon; his full attention is given to the angels instead. They represent "one God in three persons" — the Father, the Son, and the Holy Spirit, the lines of their bodies forming a full circle. The nature of each of the three hypostases is revealed through their attributes. The house, symbolizing the initial creative Will of God, is placed over the left angel who represents the Father; the Oak of Mamre, placed over the central angel who represents the Son, can be interpreted as the tree of life and serves as a reminder of Jesus Christ's death and resurrection; the mountain — a symbol of the spiritual ascent — is placed over the right angel who represents the Holy Spirit. The cup with a calf's head in the center of the composition epitomizes the sacrifice that Jesus Christ would have to make. The icon was commissioned for the cathedral located in the Trinity Monastery of St. Sergey near Moscow and remained there until the beginning of the twentieth century. After the Russian Revolution "Trinity" was moved to the State Tretyakov Gallery.

Plate 2. Andrei Rublev, "Christ the Redeemer" (1410s)
/Андрей Рублёв, «Спас. Звенигородский чин»/

Andrei Rublev is considered to be among the most prominent figures in the history of Russian art. His contribution to the art of icon-painting was so outstanding that he was made a saint by the Russian Orthodox Church. One of the most notable of his works is "Christ the Redeemer," the central part of a row of three icons known as "Zvenigorod Tier". Unfortunately, some elements of the icon have not been preserved. Nevertheless, the image of the Redeemer is full of inexhaustibly profound meaning. It is especially praised for the purity of colour, subtle tonal transitions and a beautiful light scheme. Christ is portrayed as human and yet as a source of infinite, divine inspiration; he fully embodies universal good.

Plate 3. Andrei Rublev, "Theotokos of Vladimir" (1409)
/Андрей Рублёв, «Богоматерь Владимирская»/

The celebrated Russian icon painter Andrei Rublev is credited with creating the most notable copy of the twelfth-century Byzantine icon "Theotokos of Vladimir," also known as "Our Lady of Vladimir," which itself is one of the most important Orthodox icons. The Theotokos (Greek for Virgin Mary, literally meaning "Birth-Giver of God") is regarded as the holy protectress of Russia. Although this is a copy, Rublev's version, painted for the Cathedral of the Assumption in the medieval city of Vladimir, has considerable artistic and religious significance in its own right. The icon depicts the Virgin Mary with the infant Jesus nestled against her cheek. There is no space between the Christ child and the Virgin Mary, who is seen as the original embodiment of the human soul. Their love for each other is limitless and the ultimate meaning of this scene is an expression of God's love for humanity.

Plate 4. Anonymous, "Christ Pantocrator" (the 6th century)

The icon of "Christ Pantocrator", located at Saint Catherine's Monastery in Egypt's Sinai, is considered to be the oldest surviving icon of Jesus Christ. It was created in Constantinople in the sixth century and was given to the monastery by Byzantine Emperor Justinian I. The depiction of Jesus Christ as Pantocrator (Lord Omnipotent and Judge) later became pivotal for Orthodox Christianity; in fact, most subsequent images of Christ are based on this very icon. The image is full of contemplation, peace and conciliation; Christ is presented in the act of blessing with his right hand while holding a Gospel in his left. The asymmetric features of Christ's face are believed to emphasize his dual nature as both divine and human, with the left, divine, side glowing and having a wide open eye, and the right, human, side looking darker, as though in shadow, bearing an expression of deep thought and suffering. The "two faces of Christ" can be interpreted in a different way: some theologians contend that the hard and severe features on the right side — the side on which he holds the Gospel — portray him as a Judge who sees all, while the calm and serene expression on the left — the side with the blessing hand — represents Christ in his role of Saviour.

Plate 5. Simon Ushakov, "Image of the Saviour Not Made by Hand" (1658).
/Симон Ушаков, «Спас Нерукотворный»/

Simon Ushakov was one of the most important Russian artists of the seventeenth century, being a leading icon painter and a reformer of iconographic style. He painted the icon of the "Saviour Not Made by Hand" on numerous occasions, including his first and most famous version, created for the Moscow Church of the Trinity in Nikitinki. Traditionally, icons "made without hands" were Christian icons which were said to come into existence miraculously. They therefore demanded outstanding artistic skills and craftsmanship. The icon created by Ushakov is a fine example of his distinctive and innovative style. The most striking feature is the face of Jesus Christ looking three-dimensional; this effect was achieved with the help of the elaborate technique of alternating darker and lighter tones, the smooth transition between them being accomplished during the final stages of the work.

Plate 6. Anonymous, "Golden Locked Angel" (the 12th century) /«Ангел Златые власы»/

Although having lost some of its original features over the course of time, the icon known as the "Golden Locked Angel" still shows an unparalleled level of craftsmanship. The icon takes its name from the golden highlights used by the artist to outline and decorate the locks of the angel who is believed to be one of the Archangels, probably Gabriel. The image of the beautiful, big-eyed angel full of quiet sadness is created in accordance with Byzantine aesthetic standards. As similar surviving examples indicate, the icon might have been a part of a so-called deesis row. Though the authorship of the icon and even its origin have not been fully established, the significance of the "Golden Locked Angel" is nonetheless widely recognized. The icon was discovered in the 1920s and has since become one of the most treasured items exhibited in the State Russian Museum in Saint Petersburg.

Plate 7. Anonymous, "Saint Peter" (the 6th century)

The icon of Saint Peter from Saint Catherine's Monastery in Egypt is one of the oldest icons depicting the Apostle. It was created in the sixth century in the city of Constantinople and was later moved to the monastery. The icon looks like a portrait of a real human being rather than an Orthodox image. It nevertheless contains a number of traditional Christian symbols. Peter, who is wearing a white robe and holding a cross and two rolls, is depicted as a confessor and a defender of the faith, the cross signifying his penance and dedication to Jesus Christ. The deesis row above Peter's head, with the images of Jesus Christ, Virgin Mary and John the Evangelist, records the crucifixion scene.

Plate 8. Anonymous, "The Lamb of God" (the 15th century) /«Христос Агнец Божий»/

"The Lamb of God" is a symbolic name given to Jesus Christ for the act of sacrificing himself to take away the sins of humanity; that is why he is often visually represented as a lamb. In Eastern Orthodox iconography, however, "The Lamb of God" paintings feature the Jesus as a child instead of a lamb, and the composition of the icons is directly associated with the "Divine Liturgy," the Eucharistic service of the Byzantine tradition, where a cube of bread called "the Lamb" (symbolizing the body of Christ) and consecrated wine (representing the blood of Christ) play a major part. During the religious ceremony, the bread is placed on a footed, round metal plate known as "the diskos." A thin metal frame called "the asterisk" decorated with a star, signifying the star of Bethlehem, is placed over it. The bread and the wine are later shared with those attending the sacred service. What we see in the fifteenth-century icon of "The Lamb of God" is a symbolic depiction of the above-mentioned liturgical practice, with Jesus lying on the diskos with the asterisk placed over him; the image also features two angels worshipping the infant Christ.

19

Plate 9. Anonymous, "Annunciation" from the Church of St Clement in Ohrid, Macedonia (first quarter of the 14th century)

The icon of "Annunciation" from the Church of St. Clement in Ohrid, Macedonia is based on the scene from the New Testament that describes the announcement of the coming of Christ. It is a fine example of the fourteenth-century Constantinopolitan art. At the same time, it bears a remarkable likeness to the works created by Italian artists. The icon depicts the angel Gabriel revealing to the Virgin Mary that she will become the mother of Jesus, the Son of God. The angel makes his announcement with a commanding gesture of heavenly authority, while Mary expresses both acceptance and the will to cooperate. Their faces are calm and divine. Mary's garments have the three stars commonly used to represent her eternal virginity: before, during, and after the birth of Christ. It is of interest to note that in the Late Byzantine period icons were often painted on two sides because they were intended to be carried in processions; that is why the image of the Annunciation, in fact, appears on the reverse of another icon that also portrays the Virgin Mary.

Plate 10. Anonymous, "Holy Trinity" (14th century, renovated by Tikhon FIlatiev in 1700) /«Троица Ветхозаветная», XIV в, в 1700 году поновлена Тихоном Филатьевым/

The fourteenth-century icon of "Holy Trinity", created for the Cathedral of the Dormition in the Kremlin, illustrates a story from the Old Testament titled "The Hospitality of Abraham." It portrays three angels visiting Abraham at the Oak of Mamre to let him know that he will soon have a son. Arranged in a semi-circle, the angels are having a feast. Below are smaller figures of other characters: Abraham carrying grapes on a platter, his servant sacrificing a calf and Abraham's wife, Sarah, kneading dough. The icon holds a lot of symbols: three angels personify the Trinity (the Father, the Son, and the Holy Spirit), the calf being slaughtered signifies Christ's sacrifice, while the grapes and the bread emphasize the Eucharistic nature of the scene. In 1700 the image was renovated by Tikhon Filatiev, one of the leading icon painters of the time. While preserving the original iconography, he produced an entirely new work of art by adding fine details and creating a three-dimensional effect.

Printed in Great Britain
by Amazon